NEIL A. KJOS
PIANO LIBRARY

LEVEL FOUR

PIANO REPERTOIRE

SELECTED & EDITED BY

Keith Snell

Baroque & Classical

Henson's
music center

Camarillo · Oxnard · Ventura

CONTENTS

JOHANN SEBASTIAN BACH (1685-1750)
Prelude in C, BWV 939 3
From the *Notebook for Anna Magdalena Bach*
Minuet in C Minor, BWV Anh. 121 4

DOMENICO SCARLATTI (1685-1757)
Sonata in D Minor, L. 423 6

CARL PHILIPP EMANUEL BACH (1714-1788)
From the *Notebook for Anna Magdalena Bach*
March in G, BWV Anh. 124 8
Polonaise in G Minor, BWV Anh. 125 10
Allegro 12

JOSEPH HAYDN (1732-1809)
Allegro (From *Sonata in G, Hob. XVI:8*) 13

DANIEL GOTTLOB TÜRK (1750-1813)
Gigue 14

MUZIO CLEMENTI (1752-1832)
Sonatina in G, Op. 36, No. 2
I. Allegretto 16
II. Allegretto 19
III. Rondo: Vivace 20

WOLFGANG AMADEUS MOZART (1756-1791)
Minuet and Trio , K. 1 24

LUDWIG VAN BEETHOVEN (1770-1827)
Sonatina in F
I. Allegro 26
II. Rondo: Vivace 29

FRIEDRICH KUHLAU (1786-1832)
Sonatina in C, Op. 55, No. 1
I. Allegro 33
II. Rondo: Vivace 36

Composer Biographies 40

ISBN 0-8497-6225-1

©**1997 Neil A. Kjos Music Company**, 4380 Jutland Drive, San Diego, California 92117
International copyright secured. All rights reserved. Printed in U.S.A.

Prelude

BWV 939
From *Eighteen Little Preludes*

J. S. Bach
(1685-1750)

Minuet

BWV Anh. 121

From the *Notebook for Anna Magdalena Bach*

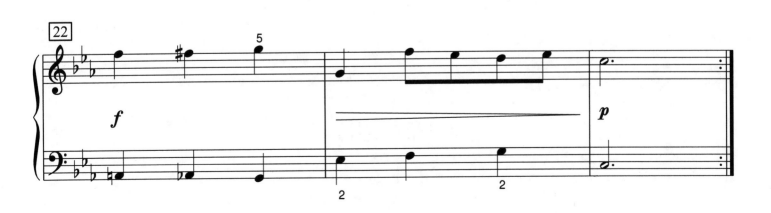

Sonata

L. 423

Domenico Scarlatti
(1685-1757)

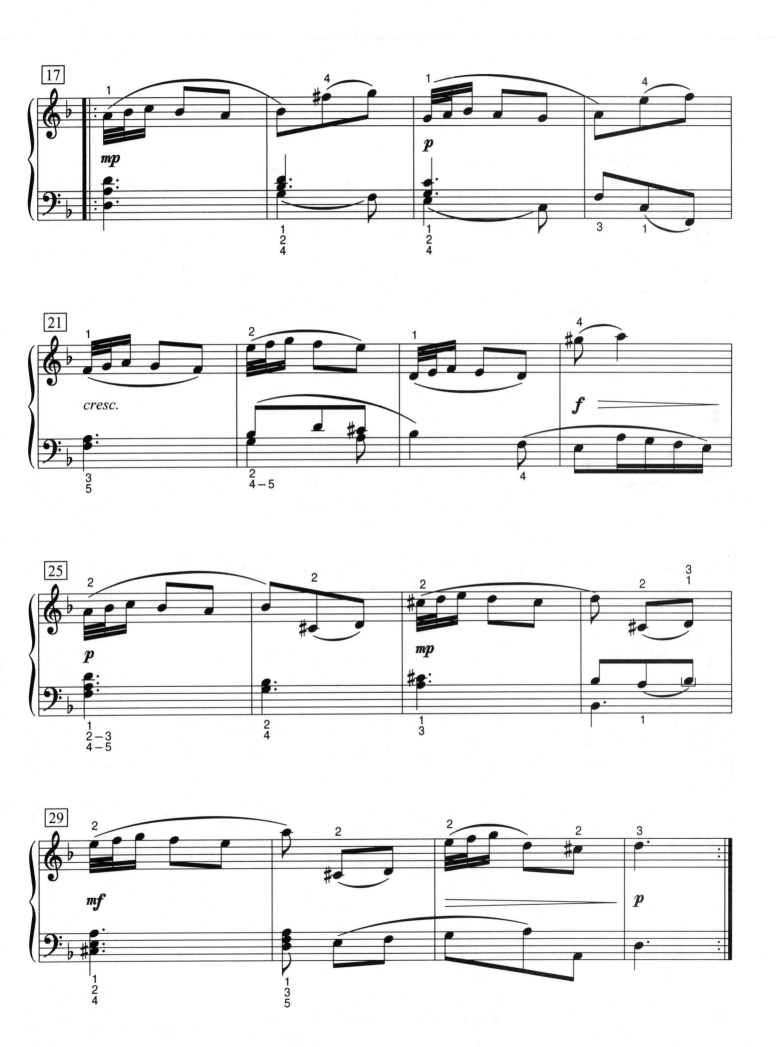

March

BWV Anh. 124

From the *Notebook for Anna Magdalena Bach*

C. P. E. Bach
(1714-1788)

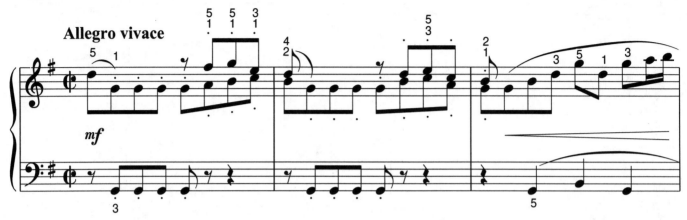

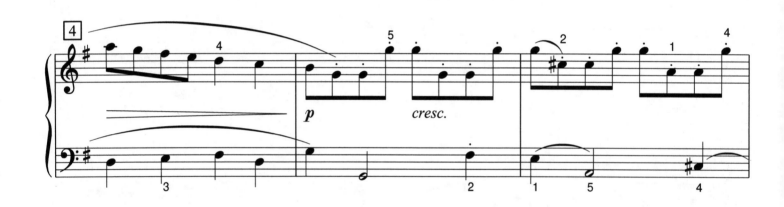

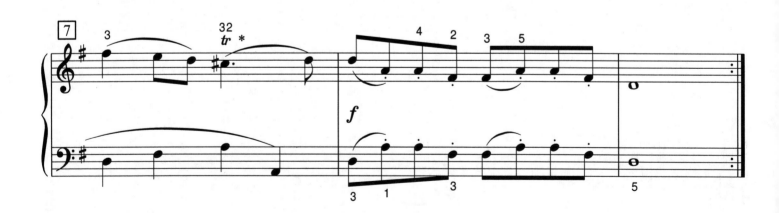

Polonaise

BWV Anh. 125
From the *Notebook for Anna Magdalena Bach*

C. P. E. Bach
(1714-1788)

Allegro

C. P. E. Bach
(1714-1788)

Allegro

From *Sonata in G, Hob. XVI:8*

Joseph Haydn
(1732-1809)

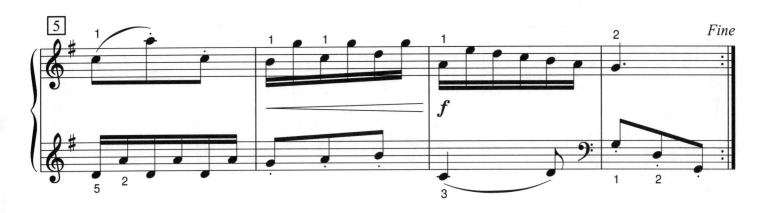

GP604

Gigue

Daniel Gottlob Türk
(1750-1813)

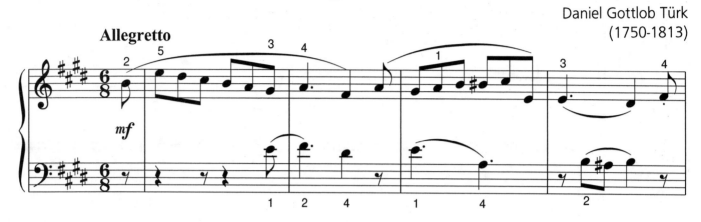

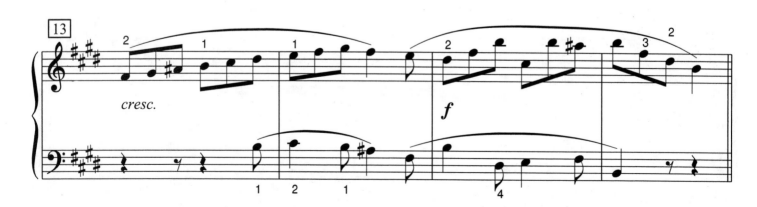

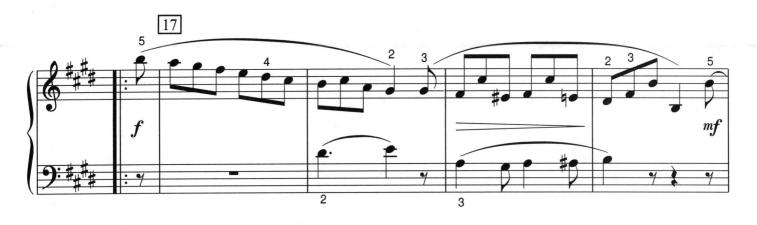

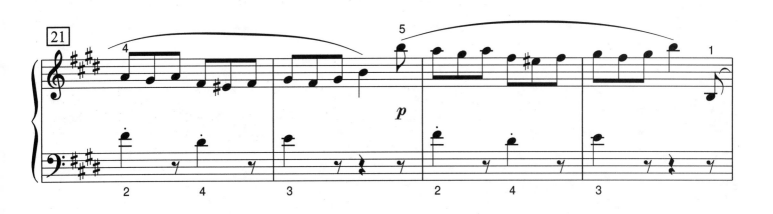

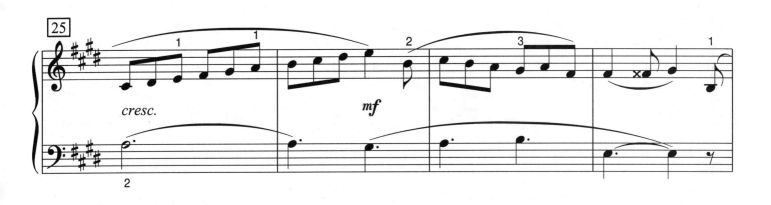

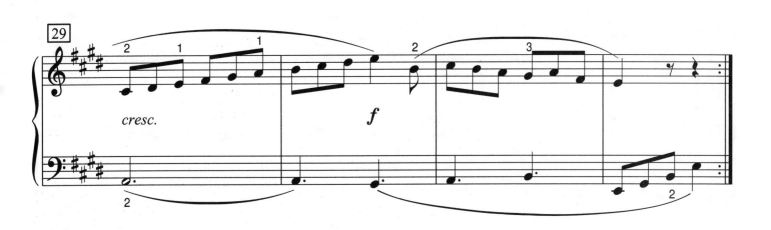

Sonatina

Op. 36 No. 2

I.

Muzio Clementi
(1752-1832)

II.

III. Rondo

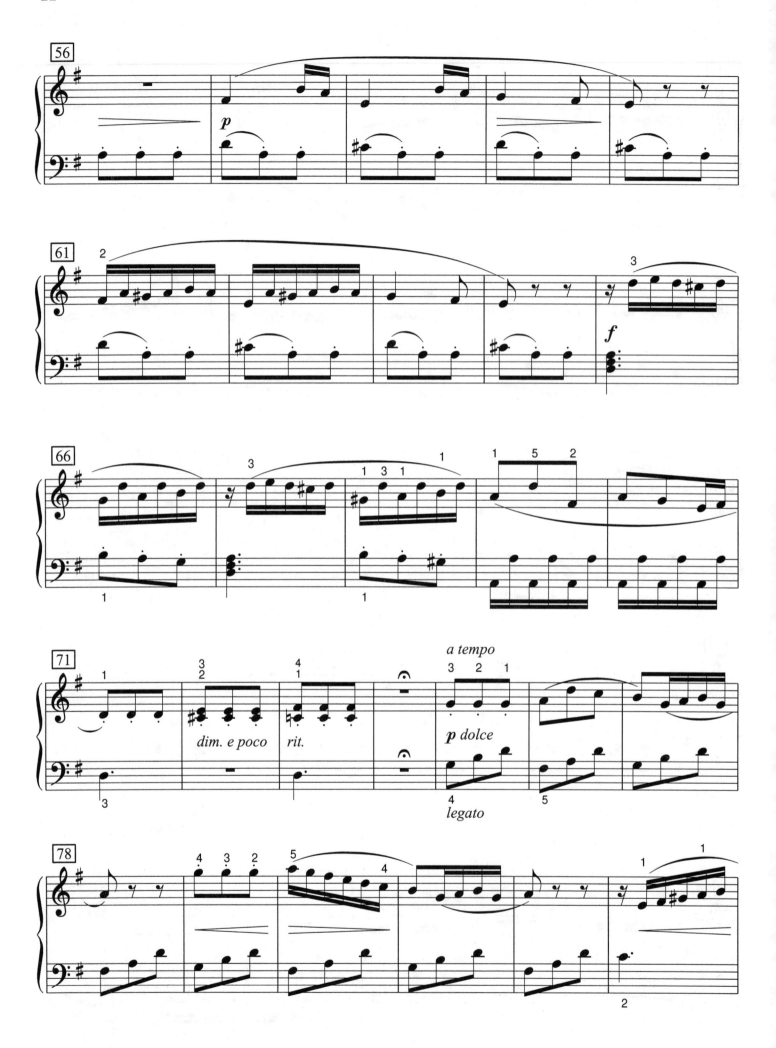

Minuet and Trio

K. 1

Wolfgang Amadeus Mozart
(1756-1791)

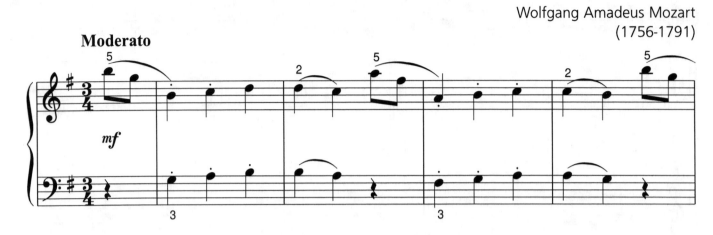

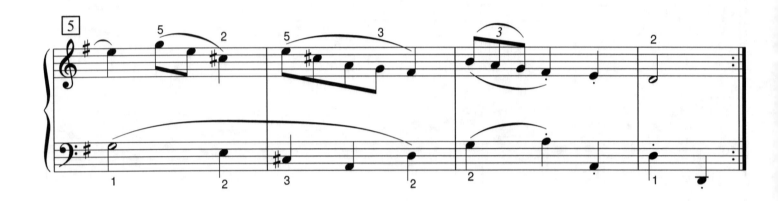

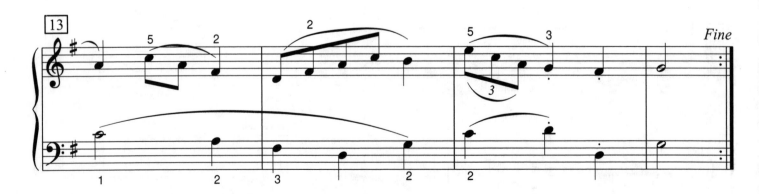

Sonatina
I.

Ludwig van Beethoven
(1770-1827)

II. Rondo

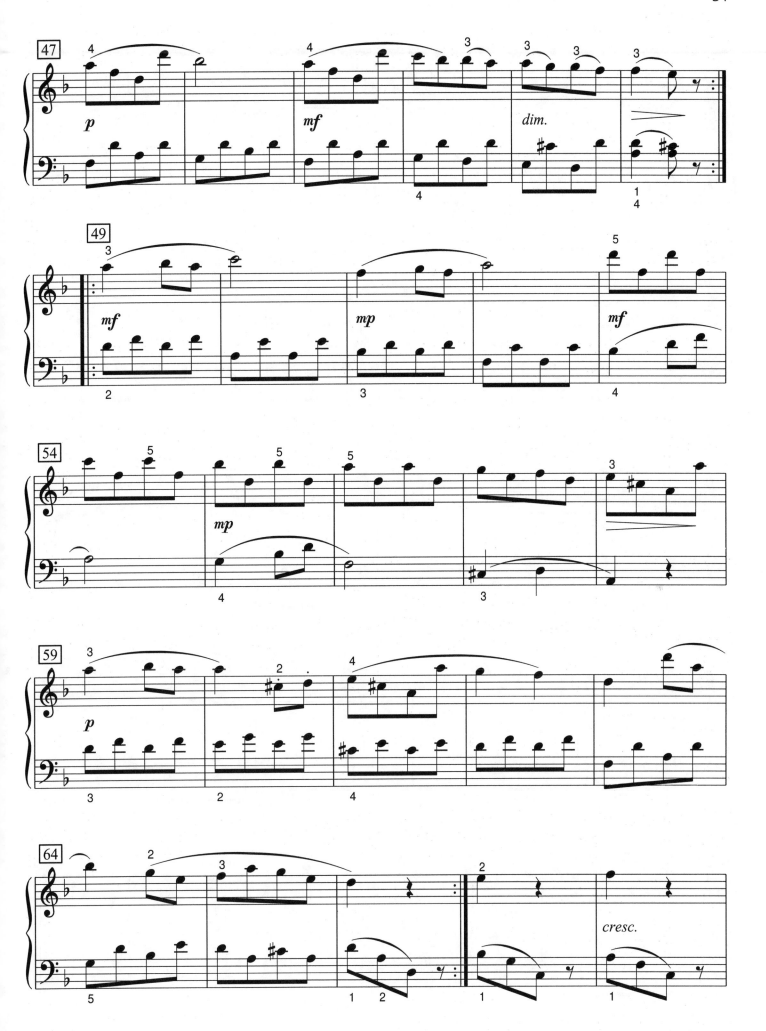

Sonatina
Op. 55 No. 1

I.

Friedrich Kuhlau
(1786-1832)

GP604

II. Rondo

COMPOSER BIOGRAPHIES

Carl Philipp Emanuel Bach (1714-1788) was a German composer and the second son of J. S. Bach. Widely acclaimed throughout Europe, he was the leading court musician of Frederick the Great in Berlin. His pre-classical style was important during the transition from the Baroque period into the Classical period. His keyboard works influenced composers such as Haydn, Mozart and Beethoven. His Essay on the True Art of Keyboard Playing is one of the first important piano methods, and a definitive source on the style and performance practices of his time.

Johann Sebastian Bach (1685-1750) was a German composer and frequently regarded as the greatest composer of the Baroque period. He had numerous relatives who were musicians: from seven generations, 193 out of 200 were musicians. Throughout his life he held positions at various churches and in royal courts, and for almost thirty years he was the director of music at the St. Thomas School in Leipzig. He was married twice and had twenty children, several of whom became well known musicians. Bach was a prolific composer; his complete works fill forty-six large volumes containing choral music, concertos, orchestral and chamber works, and organ and clavier (keyboard) music.

Ludwig van Beethoven (1770-1827), was a German composer and pianist. Beethovens father insisted that Beethoven practice long hours in hopes he would become a child prodigy like Mozart. In 1787 he visited Vienna where he played for Mozart who predicted an outstanding musical career for him. In 1792 he studied with Haydn for about a year. About this time, Beethoven began to earn his living from the sale of compositions and from teaching. He became an honored and respected musician to many royal families. In his early thirties Beethoven experienced hearing loss which later resulted in total deafness. A prolific composer, Beethoven wrote thirty-two piano sonatas, five piano concertos, one violin concerto, an opera, a great quantity of chamber music, and many other works.

Muzio Clementi (1752-1832) was a famous Italian pianist, composer, and teacher. In 1781 he and Mozart had a contest to determine which one was the better pianist. Although no winner was announced, Clementi was thought to have a better technique, but the audience felt that Mozart was a better musician. Clementi wrote The Art of Playing on the Piano-Forte which he used with his beginning students. Chopin also used this book with his students. In addition to his teaching, composing, and performing, Clementi established a successful piano factory and a publishing company.

Franz Joseph Haydn (1732-1809), Austrian composer, as a youth studied singing, violin, and clavier and became a choirboy to the Vienna Cathedral. He spent more than thirty years in the service of Prince Esterhazy, a Hungarian nobleman, at Eisenstadt. Haydn was a major influence in the development of the symphony, sonata, and string quartet. During his long life he composed approximately eighty-three string quartets, more than fifty piano sonatas, two hundred songs, 104 symphonies, eighteen operas, a vast amount of church music, concertos, and many other works.

Friedrich Kuhlau (1786-1832) was born in Hamburg, Germany where he was highly regarded as a pianist, piano teacher, and composer. In 1810, he moved to Copenhagen, Denmark. There he became known as the Great Danish Composer when he composed several successful operas which used popular national songs. In 1825, Kuhlau gained the respect and friendship of Ludwig van Beethoven during a visit to Vienna. It was on this occasion that Beethoven wrote a humorous canon on Kuhlaus name: Kuhl, nicht lau - cool, not lukewarm! Today, Kuhlau is best known for his sonatas and sonatinas for the piano and his many works for the flute.

Wolfgang Amadeus Mozart (1756-1791), Austrian composer and pianist, was a child prodigy. He was taught how to play the harpsichord and violin by his father, Leopold, and by the age of five he could play and compose pieces. When he was six, his father arranged a debut for Wolfgang. He was then exhibited all over Europe displaying his remarkable musical ability. Mozart could write a complete symphony during a stagecoach ride, or write out a complicated score from memory after one hearing. During his brief life, he wrote numerous symphonies, operas, concertos, songs, church music, chamber music, and keyboard music.

Notebook for Anna Magdalena Bach (1725) was a gift from J. S. Bach to his wife, Anna Magdalena, on her twenty-fifth birthday. He intended for her to copy into it music of her own choosing. Most of the pieces in the Notebook are in Anna Magdalenas own handwriting, therefore the identity of many of the original composers remain unknown. It is likely that the unidentified composers were family members, friends, or J. S. Bach himself.